I REACHED FOR THE SKY

OPEN DOOR BOOKS

I REACHED
FOR THE SKY

By Betty Patterson

With Margaret Friskey and Gene Klinger

Cover photos and photos on pages 2, 6, 43, 44, 55, 56, and 59 courtesy of United Air Lines.

Published by Childrens Press, Chicago, Illinois

Library of Congress Catalog Card Number 77-107498

4 5 6 7 8 9 10 11 12 13 14 15 16 17 18 19 20 21 22 23 24 25 R 75 74 73 72 71

CONTENTS

LISTEN TO ME

"What makes you think you want to be a stewardess?"

The man sounded as if he were frowning. He had that kind of a voice, all harsh and cold. I stared at the back of his neck. The sun had turned it red. All I could see were his shoulders, the patch of red neck, and the back of his head, covered with short, blond hair.

"I enjoy being with people," I said. "And I enjoy flying. Both people and flying make me feel good."

He didn't say anything. He just sat with his back to me, staring out the window.

I thought about my helicopter. No, I wasn't going to tell him about that.

I sat watching his back. I watched him for a long time before I realized what he was doing. He was watching a fly buzzing around his window screen. He just sat with his back to me, staring at that old fly.

7

There was a magazine rolled up into a tight cylinder in his fist. I kept waiting for him to swat the fly with it. But he didn't.

We'd been sitting like this for almost half an hour. The Job Corps had given me airplane tickets to fly from Los Angeles to Phoenix and back for this job interview. They'd told me that I'd have lunch with the people here and then fly back home in time for dinner. But so far I'd only been asked questions. He hadn't even looked at the résumé I'd brought. Or at me.

I felt like a stone. Like a little speck on the wall. I wanted to scream at him. To open my mouth and shout, Look at me! Look at me! I've flown all the way from California to talk with you. Turn around and look at me, please! Listen to me!

Suddenly he swung around in his chair. I was surprised when I saw that his face was so young. Somehow I had thought he was much older. "It's time for me to go to lunch. If you don't hear from us in two or three weeks, then we don't have anything. Understand?"

I understood. There was a familiar clattering sound outside as a helicopter hovered overhead. I turned and walked out of the door. The helicopter hung overhead for a moment, then spun off for the sun.

8

THE RACE

"Come on! Hurry!"

I could hear the clatter of the helicopter ringing in my ears. I hurried up the high hill. My foot slipped on a loose rock. Stumbling, I caught myself on a nearby branch and regained my balance.

I could hear the others far behind me.

"Come on! You'll miss it!"

"Betty, you're really crazy! How are we going to miss something that never was?"

"You'll see! You'll all see soon enough. If you boys could only climb as fast as this little old girl can. Boys! I thought you were supposed to be fast. Turtle's got nothing on the likes of you!"

I stretched out on the grass on the top of the hill. Below me, I could see the countryside around Macon, Georgia—the red dirt and the scrawny trees. Until I first climbed this hill, I never knew there was this much land in the whole world. From here all of

This picture of my two brothers and me was taken just before I started school.

Macon was a dollhouse-sized town that I could sit and watch. But I didn't enjoy the things I saw below me nearly as much as what I now looked for overhead.

The late afternoon's long shadows stretched across the land like low-slung, creeping cats. It would be here any minute. But what if, today of all days, it didn't come? Had I broken a secret, and in doing so brought an end to all of our afternoons? I didn't care, really, what the others would say if it never came. Their laughter wouldn't have hurt too badly. But it mattered more than anything else to know that it would never stop coming.

My fears were shattered by a slight clattering sound behind the distant treetops. The others hadn't heard it yet. But I could hear that sound even in my sleep. Jumping up, I waved my thin arms and pointed. "There! There it is!"

Over the treetops the helicopter skimmed. The pilot saw me and veered over toward the hilltop. He hovered overhead, pausing to wave down at us before he disappeared in the distance. We stared at the point where the helicopter had vanished. None of us said a word. Finally, one of my cousins broke the silence.

"You said you could touch it. You said it came so close you could touch it."

I shut my eyes and hugged my chest, smiling to myself. "I feel as if I could touch it. Someday I will. Someday I'll fly my own helicopter!"

FIRST TOY

I never did like walls or fences. Not wooden ones or wire ones or thick, solid, brick ones. I still don't like to feel cooped up, shut in, or trapped.

That is why I didn't like the wall of trees that circled our little yard. That little yard was like a hole in a doughnut. It was just a small open space surrounded by a deep woods.

It was a quiet, lonely place. I spent many hot, sunny hours there with my two brothers and my baby sister. We were not old enough to go to school, so for a long time I thought we were the only children in the world.

My mother would talk to us while she worked. She would tell us how to make things out of empty boxes. She'd found the broken spoons that we dug with in the sandy soil. There was no money for toys, but our mother could always invent new games for us to play.

We did have one store-bought toy. It was a red truck. It had no wheels. As long as I could remember

12

it never had wheels. But that didn't bother us. One day we found another truck just like ours at the dump. We brought the new treasure home, and Mother painted it bright blue, so that we could tell the two trucks apart.

One day my brothers were playing with the trucks. I sat digging in the sand. Mother was busy making an ironing board from a piece of pine. When she was finished sawing and sanding, she had a small piece of pine left. "Betty," she said, "I think it's time you had yourself a toy."

I dropped my spoons and raced over to see what she was doing. She'd cut the piece of wood apart. Then she nailed a narrow piece across the top of a wider piece, and a small triangular piece to the back.

"If that look in your eyes tells me anything, girl," she said smiling down at me from her work, "it says that as far as you're going to want to go in life, you're going to need more than a truck to take you there."

She'd finished sanding the wood, and she held it up so I could see the new toy. Its smooth wood gleamed as it balanced in her hand. "Yes, ma'am, no truck is going to take you far enough or high enough. You want to be somebody too much for that. What you're going to need, girl, is a plane."

Laughing, she handed me my new toy.

THE DREAM

I used to dream about my helicopter. When I dreamed about it, I awoke smiling and feeling as if I had been gliding through the air. I had another dream, too. But when I awoke from it, I would awake crying, and I would not be able to fall asleep again for a long time.

The other dream was always the same. I was walking down a narrow path. I was walking along very slowly. Every so often I'd pause and stare up at the huge, twisted trees that bent low over the narrow road. The trees were twisted and shaped like strange creatures. They waved their skinny faces at me and bent down closer and closer. Just when it seemed that the odd-shaped trees would surely snatch me up, I would wake up screaming.

I thought about my dream all the way to Grandmother's house. We had gotten up early that morning and made a quick breakfast. While we

Left: My sister, Minnie, when she was in second grade. Below: This picture of me was taken when I was in fourth grade.

cleaned the dishes, my mother loaded all of the clothes onto our red wagon. When it was full, she put my little sister on top of the wagon to hold down the clothes.

Then we marched out onto the narrow road and began our long trip to Grandmother's. We went there once each week. It took most of the day just to get there and back, but it was the closest place for my mother to wash our clothes.

I walked along behind the wagon, trying not to look up at the tall trees swaying in the breeze. Instead, I watched the wobbly wheels of the old wagon as they bounced from rut to rut. All along the road there wasn't another human being besides ourselves. There were mosquitoes and wild animals, but no other people.

We stopped to pick juicy red strawberries and to watch the butterflies and birds. A dragonfly circled lazily overhead. In the bushes I could see a spider hanging upside down from its thread. Both sides of the road were like giant walls. It was impossible to guess what a person brave enough to travel through them would find on the other side.

Someday I'd know. Someday I'd fly over all the walls in the world. I'd find out what was behind all of them. I stretched my arms out as far as I could on both sides. I waved them up toward the sky, then dashed them down toward the ground. I moved them up, down, and back again as I stared at my birdlike shadow on the red dirt road.

The shadows of the trees closed in over my own thin shadow. Quickly I hurried to catch up with my mother.

GRADUATION

There were some things that we didn't talk about at home. When you don't know where your next meal is coming from, it doesn't make much sense to sit around talking about wanting to fly an airplane. Some folks would say you were just selfish. Others would say you were just crazy.

But, when that was just about *all* you ever did think about, there comes a day when you've got to say something. For me, that day came three years after I graduated from high school. It was still hard to believe that I was out of school at last. I could still remember my first-grade teacher, Mrs. Ingram. She always had me read out loud from our reader. I think she picked me because I could read fast. I'd sit there and read one story after another. I don't know for sure what Mrs. Ingram did all that time, but it sure looked as if she were sleeping. Every time I came to a word I couldn't say, I'd whisper quietly, "Mrs. Ingram." She never heard me. Then I would say once again—this time a little louder—"Mrs. Ingram."

Then, when she didn't answer, I'd start to cry. I'd have to cry for quite awhile before she would jump up with a start, asking what was the matter.

Then I'd show her the word, and she'd tell me what it was, and I'd start reading all over again.

During my last year in school, I earned money by sewing clothes for my neighbors. I sewed almost all of my own clothes, too.

When school was over, I got a job in a tailor shop. After working there for three years, I knew I couldn't stay in Macon any longer, sewing clothes for other people. Though I had wanted to go away all of my life, I'd never been away from Macon or my family. Now, when I was finally about to make the decision to take that big step, it became very frightening to me.

One evening I sat watching my mother iron on her old pine ironing board.

"Mom, I've been thinking about what I should do."

"What were you thinking, Betty?"

"Well, Aunt Grace said I could get a job in Newark. And I could live with her."

"Is that what you really want to do?"

"No, not really."

"What *do* you want to do, Betty?"

"I don't know, for sure."

"I thought you'd already made up your mind about that."

"What?"

"About wanting to fly."

"I *do* want to fly. I always have."

"If that's what you want, if that's what will make things better for you, then I guess that's what you've got to do."

Ever since I was a little girl, I'd watched the big long-distance buses driving through Macon. But this was the first time I'd ever taken a long bus ride. As I watched, the familiar smiles and the friendly hands waving back at me slipped into the distance. Even the great trees that lined the road changed into a blur of green. Then they, too, vanished. Fresh fields and clear, blue skies were all around me.

NEWARK

It was early morning when we rode down the still-deserted streets of Newark. A few people were riding buses to their early morning jobs. Others were coming home from the clubs and restaurants that must have just closed.

It felt good to climb out of the bus and stretch. I found a pay phone and called my aunt.

Then I spent the rest of the morning looking for a job. I saw a sign in the front of one doorway. It was a coat factory. I went up the steps and opened the door. I could sew, I could do just about anything with a needle and thread.

"Yes? May I help you?"

I hadn't seen the small man until he spoke.

"I'm looking for work. I can sew. I made the dress that I'm wearing now."

He looked at me for a minute. "We could use you to sew fur collars on coats. Can you do that? Come back tomorrow morning then, at eight o'clock. We'll pay you a dollar and a quarter an hour."

I lasted three days on the job. It was terrible. We had to sew each collar on by hand. The work was hard, and they gave us much more than we could ever do in any one day.

That first afternoon when I left work, I began looking around for another job. Finally I found one in a blouse factory. We started even earlier in the morning. But that was all right, because we were finished at three o'clock in the afternoon. This job was almost as bad as the first. They kept pushing baskets of half-finished blouses at me. Sometimes they'd have me putting in sleeves. The next day I'd be making buttonholes.

It wasn't that the work was so hard. In fact, it was almost too easy. To seam up the arm and down the side of a blouse, you didn't even have to think about what you were doing.

The other girls would talk a lot about who they had gone out with the night before, or a fight they'd had with their family that morning. I just sat there dreaming about getting out from behind those four walls and flying, taking wing and traveling far away.

Once I made the mistake of telling the girls what I was thinking.

"Betty, you'd better stop your daydreaming."

"That's right, girl. You're never going to leave here."

"What's wrong with you anyway?"

I didn't say anything for a while. Finally I told them, "When I become a pilot, you'll be the first to know. I'll fly circles for you overhead. And you'll stick your old heads out the window to see what's going on up there, and I'll tip my wings once at you before flying off to everywhere."

I didn't say anymore the rest of the afternoon. I just kept working, trying to stay awake.

SOMETHING BETTER

One morning I saw an ad in the newspaper.

EARN & LEARN: Wanted, high school graduates between the ages of 18 and 25 to earn as they learn to be
telephone operators.

I thought I'd like to talk to people all day, even if I couldn't see them. I wore my best tailored suit to work that day. As soon as work was over I hurried to the telephone company.

But by the time I got there, the jobs were all taken. Wasn't I ever going to get a decent job? It seemed that I'd never get out of the blouse factory.

"Cheer up! There are other jobs."

I looked up to see a girl about my age smiling at me.

"My name's Hazel Black. Where are you from?"

"I'm Betty Patterson. I'm from Georgia. And if things don't get better, I might just be going back there."

"I used to live in Georgia. I don't plan on going back—no matter what. You wanted the phone job, too?"

I nodded.

"I really want to be a librarian. Only I just can't seem to find a library that's looking for me."

"I'm thinking of . . . of something better, too. I can't seem to get anywhere either."

"Maybe we should try the Job Corps. They're supposed to train you for any kind of job you want."

"Any job? Somebody must be kidding you."

"No, Betty, they really try to train you to do what you want to do."

"Maybe what *you* want. Not what *I* want."

"Are you that special?"

"If you knew what I want to do, you'd understand."

"What do you want to do? Go to the moon?"

"That would be easy. I want to fly a helicopter."

"You're putting me on."

"No. But that's what *they'll* say, too."

"You *are* serious, aren't you?"

"I've been serious about this since I was five years old. It's everybody else who's joking around."

"Well, you have to admit that it's easier to imagine you running a sewing machine than a helicopter.

Come on. The least you can do is give the Job Corps a try."

"Okay, Hazel. Which way do we go?"

"I don't know, but we can find out at the state employment office."

We stopped at a restaurant for lunch. Hazel phoned the employment office for directions.

It was mid-afternoon when we walked into the Job Corps office. A very pleasant woman talked to us.

"Sit down, Miss Patterson, Miss Brown."

Oh, oh, here it comes, I thought. I kept waiting for her to ask *that* question.

"How old are you, Betty?"

"Eighteen."

"Hazel?"

"Eighteen."

"And you're both citizens of the United States?" We nodded.

"Did you both graduate from high school?"

"Yes, but we haven't been able to go on to college."

"That's all right. Many of our applicants are high school dropouts or have finished high school but have not gone on to college. That's one of the reasons for the Job Corps. Here you can learn all you will need to be able to get a job.

"Are you both working now?"

"I'm working in a blouse factory. But I know I can do better if I get the training."

"I know you can, too. We'll be in touch with both of you as soon as we have something for you."

WAITING

The ringing of the alarm clock shattered my dream, and the helicopter dissolved into the familiar surroundings of my dimly lit room. It was barely six o'clock. I scrubbed my face with cool water, fighting back a desire to sleep for just a few more minutes. If I were going to get to work on time, I'd have to hurry.

Today, it turned out, was going to be a buttonhole day. All morning I sewed buttonholes. After lunch, there were more. The boredom, I decided, was the worst thing about this job. It had been almost two weeks since I last phoned the Job Corps people. Nearly six months had gone by since Hazel and I had filled out our applications. Every two weeks we would call, and every two weeks they would tell us the same thing. "There are ten thousand girls on the list. As soon as we get to your names, we'll phone you."

Hazel and I sometimes went to the movies or out for dinner. But most of our free time was spent looking for other jobs. She still couldn't get a job as a librarian. I still hadn't found my helicopter.

Each day my work became worse. I worked on blouse after blouse after blouse. My eyes ached. The walls seemed to be closing in. I began to feel cooped up, shut in, trapped.

It was cold when I stepped out of the factory and walked toward the bus stop. I started to button my coat. But I didn't. I wasn't going to touch another buttonhole. Not until I had to.

The telephone was ringing when I unlocked the front door that day. It was my cousin. I began to tell her that I'd decided to pack my bags and leave Newark. I had an aunt in Connecticut. Maybe things would somehow be better there. But my cousin didn't give me a chance to finish.

"Betty, listen to me! It happened! It did! Just now!"

"What happened?"

"They called! The Job Corps! They want you to fly to Los Angeles next Tuesday!"

I didn't say a word. I couldn't. I was crying too hard.

FLIGHT

Tuesday morning came slowly, a little bit at a time. I know because I stayed up all of Monday night watching. The blackness of the night turned to charcoal gray, and then into pale traces of pink. Then, suddenly into fiery oranges. I'd never seen a more beautiful morning.

Hazel and I were the first in line when the time came to board our plane. I had been watching it through a window for some time. I'd never been this close to a plane before. Men in coveralls and uniforms were crawling around under it and over it. I could see the stewardess and captain inside, moving about past the windows.

Hazel and I hurried aboard, smiled at the stewardess, and went back to our seats. We smiled at each other when we reached our row of seats.

"You take the window," Hazel said, laughing. "After all, you're going to be the pilot."

We couldn't stop talking, we were so excited.

"Hazel! We're really doing it! This is for real!"

Then we began to taxi toward the runway. I watched the stewardess as she explained how the oxygen masks worked and where the exits were. I could hear the engines and feel their vibrations as we moved along. Then the wheels of the plane left the ground. There was a loud click as they slipped up under the plane. Suddenly I was silent. I stared at the sky around me, and down below, at the streets and city blocks that grew smaller and smaller as I watched. This was no dream. This was as real as anything I had ever known. It was exactly as I had always dreamed it would be.

LOS ANGELES

The first people Hazel and I met in Los Angeles were our "big sisters." Girls who have been with the Job Corps for a while are assigned new girls to help along. Our big sisters helped us feel at home.

They were very friendly. They showed us around our new home, an old thirteen-story hotel that was now a Job Corps center for girls.

It was very nice. The girls showed us reading rooms, sewing rooms, a cafeteria, and a laundry room. They took us to classrooms, a gym, and exercise rooms. On the seventh floor they showed us a swimming pool. Then they took us to our rooms.

Here I met my two roommates. Each of us had a single bed and a chest of drawers. None of us had many clothes, so closet space was no problem.

Both of my roommates and I were farther from home than we had ever been before. Each of us got a bit homesick during the first few weeks.

But our classes kept us so busy that there really wasn't much time for feeling blue.

"You can't get a good job without knowing how to read and write and express yourselves well." For the first six weeks the teachers pounded that realization into our heads. We studied reading, writing, and arithmetic. We had all studied these things before. But there was a lot that we had forgotten, and even more that we had never been taught.

When we weren't studying we had to help keep the center going. We worked in the cafeteria. We kept our rooms and clothes in good shape.

The first six weeks went by quickly. The following day I was supposed to sit down with a counselor and decide what kind of job I was going to study for. I didn't know what to tell her. I had gone out to the airport to think.

I sat watching families and couples and lone travelers heading for their planes. Japan, Hawaii, Singapore, Rome, London—they all sounded so close. Do people really just step on a plane and a few hours later step off anywhere?

Some people do. But there was only a dollar and a half in my purse. Only enough for a bite to eat and the bus fare back to the center before bed check.

A JOB OF MY OWN

It felt good to be sitting down. I'd left the airport in time to be back by bed check, but I hadn't slept much the night before. I sat quietly while the woman who was interviewing me looked over my record. At last she glanced up and smiled.

"You've done well, Betty, this first six weeks. Now it's time for some special training. Is there a particular kind of job that you'd like to train for?"

"Yes, there is."

"Good. So many girls don't know what they want to do. What would you like to do?"

"I want to be a helicopter pilot." All night I'd practiced the words to myself. They came easily now, but almost in a whisper.

"I beg your pardon?"

"I want to be a helicopter pilot."

"I thought that's what you said." She smiled a little, but she wasn't laughing at me.

34

"Betty, I've had girls ask for all kinds of training. When we haven't been able to give it to them here at the center, I've usually known where to send them. We have contacts, you know. People who work with us."

"But for me it's impossible."

"No," she hesitated. "Nothing's impossible, Betty. But you are the first girl who's wanted to be a helicopter pilot. It *will* take some time to figure out how we're going to get you into a training program."

She sat tapping her pencil for a long while. I waited. I didn't know what to expect next. At last she looked up and said, "Betty, I'll make a deal with you. You're very good in English. If you'll go into secretarial training here at the center, I'll do everything I can to help you become a helicopter pilot. But as I said, this will take time and you just can't sit around waiting."

STALEMATE

Weeks went by while I studied my secretarial courses. Typing and shorthand came easily to me. When it came time for graduation, I was at the head of the class. Once again, it was time for an interview with the Job Corps office.

This time my counselor was all ready for me when I walked in the door. "Congratulations, Betty. I understand you're a star secretarial graduate."

"Who's looking for a chance to become a helicopter pilot," I added, smiling.

"Oh, believe me, we haven't forgotten. We've investigated every possibility of placing you for helicopter training that we know of." Her voice had become serious now, and she looked me straight in the eye.

"But you haven't been able to find anything?" I knew without her saying it that it was impossible.

"The trouble, Betty," she explained, "is that you're the only girl in the Job Corps who wants to be a helicopter pilot. The training is long and expensive. If there were several dozen girls like you, we might be able to do something. But we just don't have the money it would take to train one girl."

I knew what she was saying. One good teacher was able to train hundreds of us to be secretaries. The cost was divided among all of us. I understood. But I didn't say anything. I was too sick with disappointment.

"You have an excellent record. We can get you a good job as a secretary."

"No, thank you."

"Why, Betty? It's something that you can do well."

"But it's not something that I want to do."

The two of us stared at each other across the desk. The purpose of the Job Corps was to train people like me to do a job. They'd done that. And now they wanted me to move out and become a part of the nine-to-five world. Well, they had trained me for the wrong job. And I didn't want to go.

"Think this over, won't you, Betty?"

I said that I would, but I knew I wouldn't change my mind.

YES IT CAN

"Betty," everyone said, "it can't be done."

Well, I was convinced that it could be. And I was determined that if I had to, I would go and sit on the White House steps until I could see the president and explain to him that it *had* to be done.

And so I decided to do some digging of my own. I borrowed a friend's car and drove out to a flying school not far from Los Angeles.

I saw a woman near a hangar and called out to her.

"Hi! Who can I talk to about flying lessons?"

"You can try me."

"Do you fly?"

She nodded, smiling. "I give lessons, too."

"But not for helicopters."

"Helicopters are my first love! What's your name?"

"Betty. Betty Patterson. I'm with the Job Corps."

"That's my first name, too. My last name is Ferguson. How long have you wanted to fly a helicopter?"

I told Betty about my helicopter dream and about my determination to fly regardless of what everyone else said.

"If I were you, Betty, I would get myself a job as a stewardess. That way you could fly right away, learn a lot about planes, and make enough money to save for your own flying lessons."

At first I wondered if somehow the Job Corps had gotten to her first and told her to say that. My second thought was that it was a pretty good idea.

I learned quickly that becoming a stewardess wasn't easy, either. For a long time the airlines hadn't hired any black stewardesses. Now most of them had hired some. I was turned down by the first five airlines I tried. Their quotas were full.

"Do you want to give up?" my counselor asked me. "We can give you a good job as a secretary."

"There are other airlines. Let's try United."

The next day I walked into the United personnel office. The man who greeted me was very pleasant.

"You're single, Betty?"

"Yes, I am."

"Your weight should be fine. I can see that you don't weigh more than 140 pounds.

He asked me questions about my family, my schooling, and the Job Corps. "Why do you want to be a United Air Lines stewardess?"

"Because I like people; I enjoy being with them. And I enjoy flying."

"I'm glad you know there's more to this job than smiling and serving coffee."

He gave me some forms to fill out. I'd been accepted for training as a United Air Lines stewardess.

FLIGHT SCHOOL

"Real charm," the United instructor said, "begins on the inside. It shines through. Cleanliness and good grooming are among the most important beauty aids."

I sat listening to every word she said. Classes had begun at eight-thirty that morning. It was now one-thirty. We still had several more hours of classes to go.

Today was Wednesday. Already this week we had studied how to walk up and down stairs, how to hang a coat on a hook, how to get along with grumpy people, nervous people, frightened people, demanding people, rude people. We had studied the different kinds of planes and what it was like to fly in all kinds of weather. Today we were experimenting with hairstyles and makeup.

"Every girl owes it to herself to be as pretty as possible. She can be, if she doesn't overdo it. There's a point with makeup where you stop looking better and start looking worse..."

The United Education and Training Center is one of many new buildings on a lovely fifty-five acre park in Elk Grove Village, a town northwest of Chicago. Inside are offices, classrooms, a gym, a swimming pool, and apartments. It's like a little city of its own.

Our classes lasted for six weeks. By the end of the sixth week, we were supposed to be ready to step onto a plane and handle each passenger and any emergency that might come up.

Back at the Job Corps there were other girls who wanted to become stewardesses. I had to do well. In six weeks I had to learn all there was to learn. I was the first Job Corps girl to become a stewardess. Now others were waiting, watching. If I made the grade, then they would have a chance, too. I had to do well for all of us.

I studied my lessons until bed check that night. The next morning our class met in the mock-up room. The mock-up room looked exactly like the inside of a cabin of a real plane. There we all took turns pretending that we were passengers and stewardesses. It wasn't a game. This was an important lesson in learning how to help the many different kinds of passengers that a stewardess meets every day. Each student who was acting as a passenger was handed a card. I was chosen

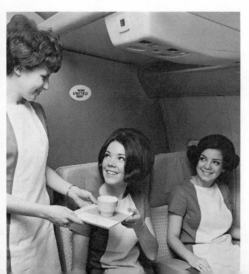

Above: During a class at the United Education and Training Center in Elk Grove Village, Illinois. Left: Part of our training to be stewardesses took place in this mock-up of a cabin of an airplane.

Right: The United Air Lines training course for stewardesses includes instruction on how to apply makeup properly. Below: During a class, an instructor explains to the girls the layout of the airplanes.

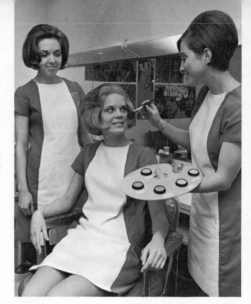

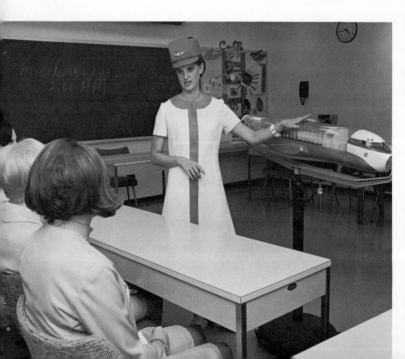

to be a stewardess, and told to welcome each passenger aboard after reading his card. The first passenger's card read: "I'm blind." Gently I guided her to a seat, talking quietly to her as I did. The next passenger's card read: "I speak only French." I smiled at her and motioned her to a seat. I would have to learn at least a few words in French.

The girl behind her handed me her card. It read: "I am crippled." I took her bag for her as she made her way down the aisle. Once she was seated I placed her crutches within her reach just beneath her seat.

WINGS

The sun sparkled on the shiny side on the DC-6. I could see the reflection of my bright uniform on the plane's brilliant surface as I stepped toward it. I knew that I was well-groomed and that my attractive new uniform fit me well. I guess I should have been quite confident and proud. I had studied for this moment for many weeks. But my knees shook and my stomach felt funny inside. Ready or not, I thought, this is my first flight.

Another stewardess met me inside the plane. We always board half an hour before the passengers do, so that we can make sure that everything is ready for them. Together we checked to see that the cabin was clean and that everything was in order. We made sure that the food shelves were full. We checked to see that the coffee was hot.

"Relax, Betty," the other stewardess said. "You'll do fine. Honestly. Just remember to smile. And to hurry! We have ninety-five people to feed in less than an hour."

Together we stood at the door and greeted each of the passengers. First, a tired businessman stepped aboard, then a nervous grandmother, a movie starlet, and a tired mother with two small children. As I greeted each new passenger, I was reminded of all the times in training when we had taken turns wearing the little signs. This was the real thing.

"I beg your pardon, sir. Kindly put your case under the seat. We may not store anything heavy on the overhead racks. Thank you."

"Here, let me help you with that seat belt. It's much too long for you. There. We shorten it like this."

"Would you like a blanket and a pillow for the baby? She may nap on this empty seat."

Every once in awhile, I would begin to do something and then panic, thinking that I had forgotten how to do it. But each time I reached out and began to do it, everything came back to me. The oxygen masks were something that in the excitement I thought I had forgotten about. But as soon as I had one in my hand everything was clear again.

The plane taxied slowly to the runway and waited for clearance to take off. The engines revved. Then the plane raced down the ribbon of concrete, gathering speed, and moments later, we were airborne over the Pacific. Within a few minutes, the pilot changed his course and headed north toward Seattle. A routine flight.

I thought of the crew in the cockpit as I went about my work. Our pilot had fifteen years experience and could handle a multimillion dollar machine like ours with cool, competent efficiency. But the passengers never saw him, or his copilot. They saw only us, their stewardesses. The grandmother glanced nervously at me as I passed, and I stopped and smiled at her. She returned my smile and leaned back in her seat.

It was some time later when I stepped out of the plane. Our passengers had left the airport almost an hour before. My feet ached like crazy, I was tired, and I had never felt happier.

FIRE!

I had been flying short hops out of San Francisco for almost two months when I faced my first emergency. Like most emergencies, it came unexpectedly.

It was, after all, just another short flight. Or so it seemed at first. The cabin had been checked, and all the passengers had been welcomed aboard. The plane, a DC-6, had just finished its taxi up the runway. We were next up for takeoff.

The other girl and I quietly checked the overhead racks to make sure that there was nothing loose up there that could fall down and hurt anyone. We were making sure that everyone's seat belt was fastened, when the word came.

One word, a sharp, one-word command barked through the plane's intercom. It went unnoticed by most of the passengers. Those who did hear it had no idea what it meant. But with that one word, the captain told the other stewardess and me: This is it—an emergency. You've been trained for this moment. Now get your passengers out of here. Fast!

The other girl and I didn't say a word. We didn't have time. Instead we busied ourselves inflating the slides for the emergency exits.

The slides were almost ready when the intercom crackled to life again. Out the side window I could see the number three engine smoking. This time the captain spoke calmly and distinctly so all of the passengers could hear.

"There seems to be a fire in one of our starboard engines. The stewardesses have prepared slides for rapid exits. But there is no hurry and no immediate danger. Everyone please step quietly to the front of the plane. Stairs are being brought out. I repeat. There is no immediate danger."

Row by row, the passengers began to leave the plane. All but one woman, who sat rigid in the back seat. She hadn't moved.

I hurried back to where she sat.

"Ma'am. We'll have to leave the plane now."

"I know. I'm just waiting to get my wig box."

"You can get off *now*. I'll get your wig box before I leave if there's time."

I helped the woman to the door and down the steps.

MR. PRESIDENT

As the plane circled, I could look down on the Potomac River, the Capitol Building, and the Washington Monument. In a few minutes we would be landing at National Airport. Instinctively, I started to stand up so that I could tell the passengers to fasten their seat belts and prepare for our landing. Then I laughed. This trip, I wasn't working. This time I was a passenger. And my own seat was still leaning backward. Straightening my seat, I took one last look at the blue Potomac and the Washington Monument before our plane swooped down on its approach to Washington National Airport. Now that we were about to land, I was nervous. Not because of landing. By now I was a real pro in the air. No, I was nervous about what I was going to have to do once my feet did touch the ground.

A cab sped me across town to the hotel where the national conference was being held. There were peo-

ple there from different poverty programs and Job
Corps programs. I had been asked to attend because I
was the first Job Corps graduate to become an airline
stewardess. I was supposed to talk for a minute or two
about my experiences. When I had boarded the plane
in San Francisco I had no idea of what I would say. I
still wasn't sure if the words would come.

They did. Somehow, my nervousness disappeared
once I stood up in front of the audience. I just opened
my mouth and told them about what had happened to
me. I told them about Macon and the blouse factory
and Hazel Black and the Job Corps. I talked about
stewardess training with United. I told them that since
I had joined the Job Corps and United Air Lines, I
had had nothing but wonderful experiences. I explained that if it hadn't been for the Job Corps, I would
never have become a stewardess. I explained that there
were thousands of girls around the country who could
do more than I had ever dreamed of—if they had the
opportunity.

Afterward, all of us were guests at a reception at the
White House. I couldn't believe that in a few short
years I had gone from Georgia to the White House.

I heard somebody mention my name. "Mr. President," the voice said, "this is Betty Patterson. Betty

was a Job Corps student and now she is a stewardess with United Air Lines."

Then I heard a familiar voice saying, "Yes, Betty, I've heard so much about you."

I didn't know what to say. All I could think of was "Yes, I've heard a lot about you, too." The President smiled and we shook each other's hands.

TODAY

Far below, I can see the shadow of our plane skimming across the red earth of Georgia. The blue-gray shadow stretches itself across a gently sloping valley. It pulls itself together into a bunched-up darker shadow as it climbs back out of the valley and over a rolling hill. Macon, where I spent so many years as a child, is only a small cluster of dots below.

"When I was a little girl, we'd climb those hills," I said to the man in one of the coach seats. "They don't look like much from here. But from down there, I thought they were the highest things in the whole world. Next to airplanes, of course."

"I'll bet it was fun," he said.

The color had come back into the man's face now and he no longer gripped the armrests of his seat. When we first took off I thought he was going to faint, he looked so frightened. I had begun talking with him right away and now most of the nervousness that he'd felt seemed to be gone.

"It was fun," I answered. "Almost as much fun as flying, once you get used to it."

I moved along the aisle, getting a pillow for one passenger, a magazine for another.

Our plane suddenly slipped inside a small cloud. Moments later it burst out the other side, its shadow once again skimming across the soil below.

Each month my flight schedule changes. When I first began flying I was based in San Francisco, and I flew a number of short hops to western states that I had never seen before. I came to know them almost as well as I know Georgia.

Now I'm based in Newark, New Jersey, and one day I'll fly to Detroit, Chicago, Youngstown, or Pittsburgh and perhaps the next day to Charleston or the tri-cities. Everywhere is home to me now, and I feel welcome and comfortable wherever I go.

It's been good to find out that the world is not just Macon, Georgia. And to discover that people are people wherever you go. It's good to realize that how folks are depends as much on *you* as it does on them. It's beautiful what a smile and a few friendly words can sometimes do.

Someday, I guess I may decide to settle down in one place. (I've seen so many great places, and each one seems to have something special to offer.) But now there are so many new places to go and different things to do.

Meanwhile, I'm saving a little bit of money each month. Who knows, someday soon I just may begin my helicopter lessons.

CAREER GUIDANCE

STEWARDESSES*

Nature of Work and Where Employed

Stewardesses or stewards (sometimes called flight attendants) are aboard almost all passenger planes operated by the commercial airlines. Their job is to make the passengers' flight safe, comfortable, and enjoyable. Like other flight personnel, they are responsible to the captain.

Before each flight, the stewardess attends the briefing of the flight crew. She sees that the passenger cabin is in order, that supplies and emergency passenger gear are aboard, and that necessary food and beverages are in the galley. As the passengers come aboard, she greets them, checks their tickets, and assists them with their coats and small luggage. On some flights, she may sell tickets.

During the flight, the stewardess makes certain that seat belts are fastened and gives safety instructions when required. She answers questions about the flight and weather, distributes reading matter and pillows, helps care for small children and babies, and keeps the cabin neat. On some flights, she heats and serves meals that have been previously cooked. On other flights, she may prepare, sell, and serve cocktails. After the flight, she completes flight reports. On international flights, she also gives customs information, instructs passengers on the use of emergency equip-

*Career information from United States Department of Labor Occupational Outlook Handbook.

ment, and repeats instructions in an appropriate foreign language to accommodate foreign passengers.

About 21,000 stewardesses and 1,000 stewards worked for the scheduled airlines in late 1966. About 80 percent were employed by the domestic airlines, and the rest worked for international lines. Nearly all stewards were employed on overseas flights. Airliners generally carry one to six flight attendants, depending on the size of the plane and what proportion of the flight is economy or first class. Most flight attendants are stationed in major cities at the airlines' main bases. A few who serve on international flights are based in foreign countries.

Training, Other Qualifications, and Advancement

Because stewardesses are in constant association with passengers, the airlines place great stress on hiring young women who are attractive, poised, tactful, and resourceful. As a rule, applicants must be twenty to twenty-seven years old, five feet two inches to five feet nine inches tall, with weight in proportion to height (but not to exceed 140 pounds), and in excellent health. They must also have a pleasant speaking voice and good vision. As of mid-1967, some major airlines still required that stewardesses be unmarried. This requirement, however, has recently been lifted by many airlines.

Stewardesses who no longer qualify for flying may obtain jobs in other departments, such as sales or public relations.

Applicants for the job of stewardess must have at least a high school education. Those with two years of college, nurses' training, or business experience in dealing with the public are preferred. Stewardesses who work for international airlines generally must be able to speak an appropriate foreign language fluently.

Most large airlines give newly hired stewardesses about five weeks training in their own schools. Girls may receive free transportation to the training centers and also may receive an allowance while in attendance. Training includes classes in flight regulations and duties, company operations and schedules, emergency procedures and first aid, and personal grooming. Additional courses in passport and customs regulations are given trainees for the international routes. Toward the end of their training, students go on practice flights and perform their duties under actual flight conditions.

A few airlines which do not operate their own schools may employ graduates who have paid for their own training at private stewardesses' schools. Girls interested in becoming stewardesses should check with the airline of their choice before entering a private school to be sure they have the necessary qualifications for the airline, and that the school's training is acceptable.

Immediately upon completing their training, stewardesses report for work at one of their airline's main bases. They serve on probation for about six months, and an experienced stewardess usually works with them on their first flights. Before they are assigned to a regular flight, they may work as reserve flight attendants, during which time they serve on extra flights or replace stewardesses who are sick or on vacation.

Stewardesses may advance to jobs as first stewardess or purser, supervising stewardess, stewardess instructor, or recruiting representative. Advancement opportunities often come quickly because stewardesses work only about two or three years, on the average, and then resign.

Employment Outlook

Young women will have several thousand opportunities to get jobs as stewardesses each year throughout the 1970s. Most of these openings will occur as girls marry or leave the occupation for other reasons. (About 40 percent of the employed stewardesses leave their jobs each year.) In addition, total employment of stewardesses will grow very rapidly as a result of the anticipated large increase in passenger traffic.

Young women interested in becoming stewardesses should realize that thousands of girls apply for this type of work each year because of the glamour attached to the occupation. Despite the large number of applicants, the airlines find it difficult to obtain enough young women who can meet their high standards of attractiveness, personality, and intelligence.

Earnings and Working Conditions

An examination of union-management contracts covering several large domestic and international airlines indicates that in 1966, beginning stewardesses earned approximately $413 to $475 a month for eighty hours of flying time. Stewardesses with two years' experience earned approximately $475 to $567 a month. Those assigned to piston flights usually earned approximately $30 a month less.

Stewardesses employed on domestic flights averaged $466 a month in late 1966; those working on international flights averaged about $555.

Since commercial airlines operate around the clock, 365 days a year, stewardesses usually work irregular hours. They may work at night, on holidays, and on weekends. They are usually limited to eighty hours of flight time a month. In addition, they devote up to thirty-five hours a month to ground duties. As a result of irregular hours and limitations on the amount of flying time, some stewardesses may have fifteen days or more off each month. Of course, some time may occur between flights while away from home.

Airlines generally use the seniority bidding system for assigning home bases, flight schedules, and routes. Stewardesses with the longest service, therefore, get the more desirable flights.

The occupation of stewardess is exciting and glamorous, with opportunities to meet interesting passengers and to see new places. However, the work can be strenuous and trying. A stewardess may be on her feet during a large part of the flight. She must remain pleasant and efficient during the entire flight, regardless of how tired she may be.

Most flight attendants are members of either the Air Line Stewards and Stewardesses Association of the Transport Workers Union of America, or the Stewards and Stewardesses Division of the International Air Line Pilots Association.

Where To Go for More Information

Information about job openings in a particular airline, and the qualifications required may be obtained by writing to the personnel manager of the company. Addresses of individual companies are available from the Air Transport Association of America, 1000 Connecticut Ave. NW., Washington, D.C. 20036.